FOOT POLARITY THERAPY

FOOT POLARITY THERAPY

A Practical Introduction to Energy Balancing of the Feet

by Wilfried Teschler

Gateway Books, Bath

First published in English in 1988 by
GATEWAY BOOKS
The Hollies
Wellow
Bath, BA2 8QJ

First German publication 1985
as Das Polarity Fussbuch
by Schangrila of Durach-Bechen

Photographs by D. Niemann

Translated by Pat Campbell

Cover design by Studio B, Bristol
Set in 11pt on 12 Century Schoolbook
by Action Typesetting of Gloucester
Printed and bound by Wheaton of Exeter

British Library Cataloguing in Publication Data:
Teschler, Wilfried
    Foot polarity therapy
    1. Massage
    I. Title   II. Das Polarity Fussbuch. English
    615.8'22 RM723.C5

ISBN 0-946551-41-3

Table of Contents

Introduction

This book is an introduction to a new and very effective type of foot massage. This method of energy balancing is based on polarity therapy, and is a practical application of the knowledge that both body and mind are reflected in a person's feet. It is, therefore, possible by means of this method to have a positive influence on the conservation and flow of energy in that person as a *whole*.

Anyone who is even slightly sensitive to the finer energies in the human being will be able to carry out this treatment. Certainly constant practice and a high level of attention will be necessary, especially at the beginning, so that later on you can work confidently and reliably with this method. The more you allow yourself to be carried along and guided by the life energy, the simpler, more relaxed and more effective the massage will become.

The person being treated will notice definite changes in his life, which will become easier, fuller, kinder, and more harmonious. The aim of polarity foot therapy is to achieve a deep and ever widening harmony of thought, feeling and action.

Mönchengladbach
September   1984

1.

Polarity

1. Polarity

Polarity therapy, which is based on the yin-yang principle of balancing opposing energies (positive/negative; masculine/feminine), is a method of releasing people from physical and mental blocks, and giving them the possibility of wider and deeper self-development.

In polarity therapy we work with the help of the life energy (chi or prana), by recognising and submitting ourselves to the law of energy flow, and making use of the resulting opportunities for achieving greater balance.

The life energy, which flows between the two poles (yin and yang) can easily be experienced. Put down this book for a moment and hold out your hands at shoulder level with the palms facing. Perhaps you will immediately feel a slight tingling in your fingers and/or your hands. Breathe calmly and quietly — this encourages the flow of energy between your hands. Now move your hands wide apart. You will find that beyond a certain distance the flow of energy can no longer be felt.

Now move your hands towards each other again, to the point where the tingling is strongest. Sometimes the flow of energy is indicated also by a feeling of warmth, a pulling sensation in the fingers or by a feeling of lightness or heaviness. If you now ask someone to place his hand between yours, the energy will probably flow first over his skin, then through it and then through his whole hand.

The life energy finds its own way even through material

objects, and in doing so it releases obstacles and blocks which would have led to an inward lack of balance. What remains is harmony − a free flow of life. This is the way and at the same time the goal of polarity therapy.

In and around you there is a constant flow of vital energy. This flow is interrupted, reduced, forced back, confined or halted altogether by our human weaknesses, our mechanical blocks. The result of these blocks is inward and outward disharmony, 'problems', dullness; in short, human suffering.

Blocks restrict us to thinking, feeling and acting in a rigid, materialistic way. Unless they can be removed, we are forced into a rigid pattern of provocation and reaction, which, if we identify with it, we mistakenly take to be our own individual model of behaviour.

Polarity therapy uses the help of the life energy to remove these blocks, providing the possibility of gradually developing freedom and self-fulfillment. The aim is as follows, to achieve:
- a free flow of vital energy
- reaching the centre
- being in the centre
- harmony of body and mind
- being healthy and happy
- being confined neither in the past nor in the future
- being here and now

These are all ways of describing a state which cannot really be expressed in words, but can only be experienced and lived.

Polarity and Life Energy

Stagnant energy, which blocks the life energy, was itself formerly free-flowing vital energy. Its flow was impaired by some experience of individual stress or trauma which reduced consciousness. The stressfulness of the block depends both on the intensity of the experience and on the degree of consciousness or its absence.

If it were possible to have full consciousness, then a particularly stressful experience may have very little influence on the flow of vital energy. However, if the person is at a low level of awareness, an insignificant event, which another person would hardly notice, may arrest the flow of vital energy altogether.

Consciousness and the life energy serve one another. The level of consciousness influences the quality and amount of the life energy.

The life energy is an ever-flowing fountain of youth, which is never exhausted. It is nothing less than boundlessness and vitality. Life energy, unaccompanied by conscious awareness, is like a multi-coloured world of the emotions, like a firework continually sparkling in the most beautiful colours. If it flows along without consciousness, it is just formless and chaotic creativity, without sense or purpose.

Consciousness without vitality is like a functional house, designed and built according to purely objective criteria. It is entirely practical, but it lacks the colour and variety which people would call beautiful, vital and wonderful. This life energy promotes consciousness and enlivens it with its endless variety.

Any situation where a reduction in consciousness coincides with some stressful experience will leave its mark on the life energy, which may even become blocked. This is seen in four ways:

It will bring about a physical change corresponding to an
    area of weakness in the body.

Thought, feeling and action are forced into a rigid pattern.

As a result of what has happened, consciousness will be
    reduced for as long as the effect lasts.

The free flow of energy is stopped.

Change in physical form, mental rigidity and dullness are all
the result of structures which leave their mark on the level of
physical energy. Almost everyone will take these structures
to be his own ego-identity, his own way of living, his
strengths and weaknesses.

However, these structures contribute nothing to that
person and are even a hindrance to him. They form his
identity, the mask or persona, from behind which he only
seldom peeps out. The very word 'identity' implies the
identification with a mask. People will then say things like:
"I am a social worker, I am this and that ..., I am
restless/calm, I am kind, good/bad," etc. Attitudes which
arise as a result of mechanical structures are: "I must ... I
can't ... I wouldn't do such a thing ..." and these lead to
corresponding action signals.

The human being is made free by being liberated from his
blocks.

One view is that these blocks are present in principle
throughout the whole body. Another view is that each block
has 'its' definite place in 'its' corresponding organ of the
body.

Both views are justified. A block, no matter where it is
situated, can colour and direct a person's whole body and his
entire life. A block can dictate the how, why and wherefore
and the very goal of existence.

14

2.

The Feet
as a Mirror

2. The Feet as a Mirror

Taking the feet as a mirror we can reach the basic, underlying structures of the body.

The distribution of energy in the body corresponds to the distribution of energy in the feet. (diagram p 20)

Exercise with a partner: Experiencing energy

Hold one of your partner's feet in both your hands. Without any expectations, note the effect which the nature and sensation of his foot has on you.

Hold the foot in your hands as if it were something entirely new to you. Now become aware of the structure of the foot, its bones, joints, tendons, muscles, arteries, nerves, skin and nails. You may find it easier to do this with your eyes shut.

When you have got to know the foot better, let a picture of it come into your mind. This is a passive process, without any conscious thought or emotion on your part. The picture will arise of its own accord if you don't force it through your own wish or imagination, but as an image of the energy structure of the foot. Provided that you have let this picture emerge without using your 'head' or your own imagination, you can assume that it reflects the state of energy of the foot and is, therefore, a reflection of this person. Although this picture is happening in your mind it is formed from information from

Unity

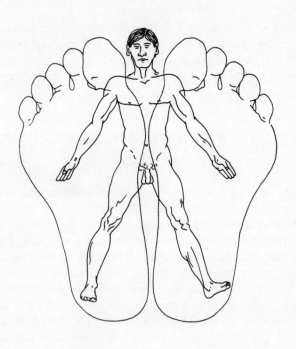

the foot itself. The picture is a translation of its energy structure.

Some people feel and experience the energy itself, others see it, and yet others know where it is and what it is like without seeing or feeling it. No matter how you perceive it, the important thing is your ability to free yourself from prejudices and expectations and from your own subjectivity, so that you allow space for impartial perception from within yourself.

A completely healthy foot may assume, to you the observer, no definite structure other than the biological form with its flow of vital energy. Any deviation from this healthy energy process is a sign that there is a block in the flow of energy.

Experiencing the Energy of the Feet

The energy patterns of different functions and of the various organs of the body are reflected in the feet.

With the aid of polarity foot therapy, we can recognise when these energy patterns form mechanical blocks; we can activate and experience them, that is to say bring them back into consciousness, blunt their effectiveness and, by means of continued polarity work dispose of them altogether.

Horizontal Correspondences

If the foot is divided horizontally, the heel region corresponds to our earthbound condition. This region gives information about our adherence to earthly existence, or about our freedom from it, communicated through the rigidity or looseness of the heel.

The middle part of the foot corresponds to the life content. This region of the foot reflects the inward and outward condition of life, the quality of life of the person concerned.

The region between the ball of the foot and the toes, and the toes themselves, correspond to the psychic makeup of the person.

The front part of the foot gives information about the quality of the relationship between the psyche and reality. In most people the toes at least are cold. This means that the psyche is 'supercool', it does not have enough energy to be connected to reality, to the earth.

Horizontal Correspondences

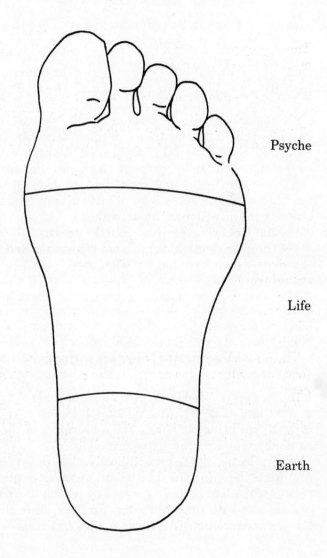

Psyche

Life

Earth

Comparing the Right and Left Feet

The left foot contains the latent potential of the individual and all the questions he has about life, as well as the problems connected with them. This foot brings with it the past, which the right foot converts into the present moment, indicating the direction of the future. The right foot gives form to the world, the plan of which is latent in the left foot.

If some abnormality is present in the heel of the left foot, but not in the right one, then a problem of an earthly kind is indicated, but has not yet actualised. If this problem is visible in the right foot and is present on the level of energy, this concrete question, which has not yet been solved, will determine that person's present form of expression and will indicate the direction of the path ahead.

The left foot brings the past into the present. The right foot takes the questions which have not yet been solved, that is to say those which have not yet been experienced, with it into the future.

The present is the pivot, where past and future meet.

Vertical Correspondences

If the feet are divided vertically, the inner side of the left foot and the inner side of the right foot will represent the passive, inward, yin principle, while the outer sides of the feet correspond to the yang, or active principle.

As a reflection of the physical body, the yin part of the foot comprises the spine, the internal organs and the glands. This region of the foot is characterised by its relative softness in comparison with the outer edge. Further, since this half of the foot is curved, there is a certain amount of space between

Vertical Correspondences

Yang   Yin

Summary of the Correspondences

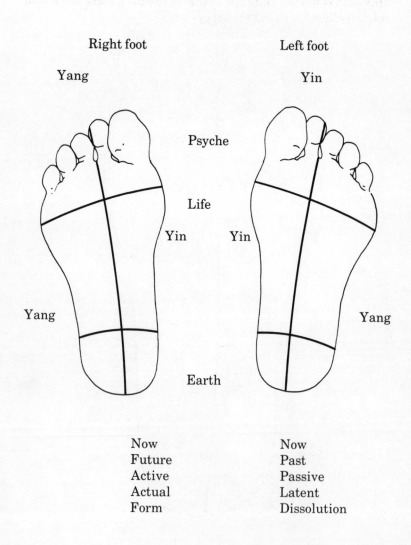

Right foot

Yang

Left foot

Yin

Psyche

Life

Yin Yin

Yang   Yang

Earth

Now	Now
Future	Past
Active	Passive
Actual	Latent
Form	Dissolution

it and the earth, a distancing from worldly events.

The outside edge of the foot is quite different. In a healthy foot there is complete contact with the earth and with reality. This part is harder than the inside of the foot. Here are found points reflecting the external organs.

Energy Points (Elements)

The Life Energy (fire)

The region indicated on the diagram "a" opposite is neither yin nor yang. It is the region of concentrated life energy. It is neutral, neither positively nor negatively charged. The primordial substance of all life lies hidden in this point.

This point represents life, vitality in material things and in the human being. It lies significantly on the line which divides and at the same time unites the earthly region and the region of the life of man. It touches equally the yin and yang halves of the foot.

Consciousness (water)

Another region of the foot which shows neither a yin nor a yang charge is the pont of consciousness/clarity (diagram "b" opposite). It lies on the vertical line which touches and divides the regions of psyche and of life.

Many people have thick, horny skin in this region. This may be taken as a sign of consciousness not fully developed, as a refusal to extend consciousness to earthly, everyday things. Tension in this region is a sign of a lack of consciousness or of a 'conscious' desire of the mind to keep aloof, a rigid retreat from worldly things.

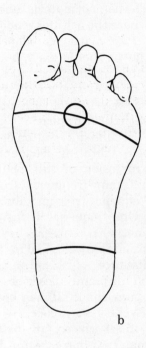

The Point of
Consciousness (water)

b

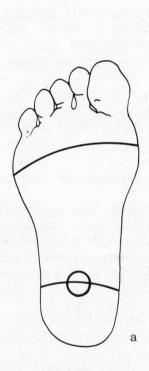

a

The Life Energy
Point (fire)

Matter (earth)

The point of material energy lies above the ankle, at the place where the achilles tendon and the calf muscle meet.

Pure matter is independent of our life, but it is essential that it should exist, before human life can receive a body. Pure matter is composed of atoms and molecules which vibrate at a certain frequency at balance within itself; it has no life yet is not without energy, has no consciousness, yet is with its own spirit.

Each manifestation of matter we know in daily life has its own vibrating frequency. Each object is a part and an expression of this primordial material. A flower has a different frequency from a stone, man has a different frequency from an animal.

One frequency is faster, another is slower: one is finer, another is coarser. They differ in the distance apart of their atomic particles and in the speed with which they reduce this distance.

This picture describes material power, which has already taken shape. It has been formed in accordance with the psycho-genetic code.

If all spaces, all distances disappear, then that which remains is pure matter. In a counter-movement, this density of matter gives rise to the whole multiplicity of life. We can look on this primordial material power as the pre-genetic code, as the potential of all that is formed. It is the material zero point containing all the possibilities of form, limitless, without information about the future or the past.

If this point at the end of the achilles tendon and the beginning of the calf muscle is pressed, almost everyone will have some sort of reaction.

Pressure on this point usually produces pain or the consciousness of being devoid of feeling. You often feel too much tension on the surface of the body or else scarcely any tension

The Point of Matter (earth)

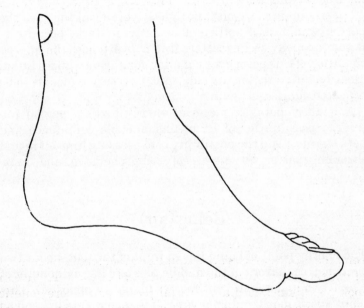

at all. If the place is too soft, without definite structure, you can assume that this person is cut off from the primordial source of matter. If the place is over-tense, as firm as steel, without any possibility of movement, then that person will be imprisoned in matter. He will no longer have any possibility of movement of his own accord. Any movement which does take place, how it resolves and its goal, will be dictated by force of circumstance.

If the point is over-soft it is, figuratively speaking, as if the person cannot reach sufficient formative material because he is too far away from matter. If it is overtense, the energy condition of this point does not allow for any new and original creation, but only for the old, rigid, uncreative models to be repeated again and again.

A healthy point of material energy gives a person unlimited possibilities of form, unshakeable confidence and perseverence and the possibility of expressing himself in and through matter by means of comprehensive and inexhaustable creativity.

Being (air)

The energy point of being lies in front of the foot, about two centimetres in front of the middle toes and has a diameter of about two and a half centimetres (diagram opposite). This point, too, is neither yin nor yang. It is as complete in itself as are the other three kinds of pure energy.

If the energy of this point remains in its indefinable, original state, that person has arrived safely at his life's goal. In that case he, too, can no longer be defined, he is all and nothing, unlimited and now.

Imbalances in and around this point indicate imbalances in the a person's state of being, his basic questioning about life. They are the essential questions which this man asks of humanity on life's path into the present.

The Point of Being (air)

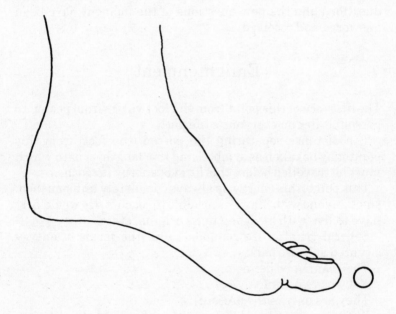

In front of the left foot, appropriately with its yin character, will be found questions which have been brought from the past into the present; and in front of the right foot, in accordance with its yang character, those questions in the present which lie ahead pointing to the future.

These two points cannot function correctly, that is to say they cannot be in their original condition, until the old questions and the new questions of the moment have been answered and resolved.

Enlightenment

The distance of this point from the foot varies from person to person. It lies on everyone's life path.

The distance separating the person (the foot) from this point may be taken as symbolising the 'length' of path which must be travelled before this form of energy is reached.

This point, this energy, is always completely unblemished, since anyone with 'flaws' is not able to reach it. He would first have to live with his being in its original state.

Several criteria are common to all the forms of energy situated at these points:

They cannot be defined.

They have no limits.

They are only in the present.

With the exception of the condition of enlightenment, they are the different paths to a single unity and bear its stamp in different ways.

They are themselves.

They can be experienced.

The original conditions of these energies are always present in all their purity. It is the blocked, retained energy within us which prevents us from experiencing them.

It is attachment or aloofness on the level of matter.

It is constriction or excess of spontaneity on the level of energy.

It is supervision or dullness on the level of consciousness.

It is rejection or greed on the level of being.

It is imagined distance or nearness on the level of enlightenment.

The easiest kind of energy for us humans to reach is life energy, which surrounds everything. With its help and according to its laws, we can, little by little, release our blocks.

In polarity foot therapy, we approach the basic underlying blocks, and with the help of life energy release them from their attachment to, or aloofness from, matter; make them conscious by removing their supervision or dullness and recognising them in their reality we recognise ourselves in our own being on the 'way' to enlightenment.

3.

Balancing Energy through the Feet

3. Balancing Energy through the Feet

The feet are for a human being the 'chief organ' for balancing the inner reserves of energy and achieving harmony with the earth's energy.

If the inner energy is depleted it is through the feet that the required energy can be obtained or, in the case of overloading, the surplus, static energy can be released.

The feet are the basic energy regulators of the body, since they reflect the energy condition of the whole body and they maintain the closest and most direct contact with the earth.

Between the poles of yin (earth) and yang (humankind) there is a continual flow, a continual exchange of energy, which maintains each pole as it is, in its own character. However, during the course of the development of energy, the poles melt, they dissolve into flowing energy, arising but also disappearing again every moment.

The earth, if only by its very existence, offers itself every moment for this exchange. It is only the human who finds it difficult to adapt him/herself to the earth, to reality. Most people hold themselves aloof from matter, declaring that their lives are independent of it and thus they distance themselves ever further from their bodies, their surroundings, their fellow men and themselves.

They become more and more top-heavy, seeking to solve the questions posed by matter on their path through life by sheer mind-power. They do not pay attention to the signals their bodies give them. They cannot come to terms with their body, rejecting it as a *thing* burdened with difficulties and fears.

The further the human spirit withdraws from matter, the more unfeeling, unsound and inhuman the whole person will become. There will be a rift between physical sensations and deeper feelings, and any emotional and physical movements which arise will be dismissed as irrational.

Direct contact with oneself and with the world will be replaced by top-heaviness and the accompanying imaginings of a world of fantasy.

If the mind and body come together, they will, in and through their unity, transform that individual into a vital, sociable person, who lives *his own* life and goes *his own* way, taking complete responsibility without feeling this to be any kind of burden. Body and mind are then no longer antagonistic nor are they dualities separated from each other, but they have become a unity of body and mind, melting into one another in mutual service.

If body and mind have, by some process, returned to their natural unity, that person will be realised in body and mind. Mental fantasy, separated from the body, will no longer hold sway, nor will physical gratification, but the emphasis will be on the recognition and preservation of the body/mind unity.

Since energy blocks on both levels have been removed or laid aside, the result is a basic general feeling of well-being. The unity of body language and mental expression is the outwardly visible sign, which can be witnessed by others, of the vital harmony within. The movements of a body-and-mind person are graceful, unhampered and unequivocal. Such a person is living the integration of body and mind.

The body-and-mind person has overcome imprisonment in matter by submitting himself to it and fulfilling it through his own nature. He has left behind him the dictates of limiting and hampering unrealised thoughts by literally allowing them free rein.

If unity of body and mind is reached and stabilised, then that person will find his true place in the world and in himself. Inward and outward conflicts will diminish appreciably, communication with others will no longer be predominately by way of the head or by way of the body, but will be freer from discussion, simpler and less restricted. That person will have become mature, fearless, and adult.

I do not consider it possible to desire this quality and to obtain it on one level only, either in the body (emotion) or in the mind (understanding). This is because it is through the unity of body and mind that inner and outer stability is reached, which neither the body nor the mind can grasp and realise by itself. Desire and longing for this unity are present in the heart, but the heart's desire and longing can give only a suggestion of this unity of body and mind, just a quick glimpse of it.

If energy can flow freely between the yin and yang poles on the plane of energy, unhindered by any blocks, then the true natural polarities for that person are realised. Each pole, in harmony with its former counterpart, has achieved its original purpose and full function.

That person has reached the inward unity* of head and feet and the outward harmony* of mind and matter.

Progress towards integration of body and mind can be achieved through the feet. There are two complementary ways of achieving this: there is the way of exercises performed alone and the way of massage with a partner. (Polarity massage is introduced and explained at length later on in this book.) In the pages which follow, I will describe the exercises to be performed alone.

*The expressions unity, harmony etc. reflect only one aspect of the integration of the body and mind. They describe this specific state from a certain point of view.

Walking

We walk with our feet.

Everyone would agree with this simple statement. From the purely anatomical point of view, there is no doubt that we walk with our feet; but on closer inspection one realises that many people walk with their heads, their shoulders, their pelvis or their stomachs. In that case, the feet merely perform the purely external functions of moving and weight-bearing.

The feet do not, in that case, realise the potential which resides within them (of treading the true path through life), but merely give form to the orders and content of other inferior parts of the body. The path through life will be coloured by the capacity of the parts of the body which give the orders.

Correspondences with all levels of the body are found in the feet. It is, therefore, possible for too much or too little emphasis on any one part of the body, with its corresponding association in the feet, to be reflected in the placing of more or less weight on certain regions of the feet; as well as in the positioning and form of the feet and finally, on the level of energy, in their very structure. The placing of more or less weight on a foot, the form of the foot, and the energy structure, form and content of the part of the body which these reflect are up to a certain point dependent on one another.

Even if a person's foot is physically/biologically irreparably deformed, it is possible for him to free himself from this deformity on the content and energy levels.

The mind-body separation will be reflected in the feet in just the same way as the super-charging of the internal organs or the extremities with energy and emotion. Changes in the harmonious structure of the person himself, his body or his feet, will be definitely noticeable in his walk, in the way his weight is distributed, the form and energy structure of his feet. These changes will be latent in his left foot, but immediately present and acting as a signal in his right foot.

The degree of development towards harmony may be deduced from the inward and outward harmony of the feet.

Walking in Harmony

Harmony is achieved by inwardly striving to create harmony, recognising temporary blocks (in oneself), adopting a positive attitude towards them and either resolving them (yang) or accepting them (yin).

If complete harmony, grace and perfect balance have been achieved, then all subjective thoughts, feelings and actions, that is to say all lack of well-being and all suffering, will have ceased to exist. Daily worries will have lost their explosive power and the 'knowledge' will have developed that it is unquestionably necessary to get rid of them.

A person in harmony is light, power, consciousness and to an equal extent body and mind. All distinction between the qualities of body and mind will have disappeared, since all polarities in him will have become united and will be flowing freely.

A simple and easy variation of the way to reach harmony is to walk with the inner, heartfelt conviction that this harmony is going to be accomplished. No matter where you go, the important thing is your inner attitude, proceeding from the heart, your inward effort to reach harmony *itself*.

In this way you will discover the basic blocks, and obstacles on your path through life, which will then gradually be resolved through knowledge, vital energy, affirmation of life and a disposition towards harmony.

Exercise: Experiencing Harmony

Stand up, preferably without shoes, and direct your attention into your feet. Consciously become aware of your feet, of how they are at the moment. When your attention is completely focused in your feet, then walk. You can either let your feet guide you to harmony (yin), or you can purposefully direct yourself towards harmony (yang).

Both 'techniques' are suitable and lead to harmony, since with both of them the blocks and consequently the obstacles on life's path can be recognised, activated and resolved.

In each case the result is the same: harmony, which is neither yin nor yang, but both powers united equally.

It is the steady flow of life.

Earthing

When standing most people do not put their weight equally on the whole of their feet.

How the weight is distributed often tells something about a person's personality and their way of life. Generally speaking, the distribution of weight shows how the *whole* person is earthed. Their quality of earthing is also revealed in the sensitivity of the foot. If the foot is relatively insensitive even if it appears to stand firmly on the ground, it will not really be firmly and permanently earthed.

Earthing takes place through contact of the foot with the earth. But true earthing involves the flow of energy between the earth and the whole person.

By becoming more aware of this inward exchange of energy with the earth, one can make oneself more independent of circumstances which cannot easily be changed, such as certain illnesses or deformities. Instead these adverse physical conditions can be transformed, allowing one, through spiritual development, to become a more balanced person.

Any kind of spiritual change must also involve the physical body, which being the vehicle we adopt in incarnation must always form the basis of the development of a well-balanced, harmonious individual.

An earthly existence brings with it the limitation of matter, and therefore of the body, which everyone must sooner or later accept if he is to make any spiritual progress.

But people tend to become identified with physical form and especially physical abnormality ,and feeling trapped, yearn for escape. The result is suffering, which can be overcome only if the person concerned is completely conscious of his own ground, of matter and corporeality, and comes to terms with it. It is only then that, in spite of any deformity which may exist, a man is present body and mind in his own being, (simultaneous adherence and opposition are what hamper development, not the illness or deformity itself).

A person is well when his body and mind are in harmony with his thought, feeling and action. This is possible even for someone with severe physical disabilities. The grounding of energy is the most contributory factor.

Polarity therapy, therefore, does not of itself cure any illness. Like yoga, tai-chi and a macrobiotic diet, it helps a person to become whole by balancing the psychic and material polarities.

If the energy imbalance of man and earth is corrected and the polarity attains harmony, then that person *is* earthed, since he has overcome the earth and his own psyche. Such a person is without any basic anxiety. He stands on his own two feet in life — he is in life, he is life itself.

Exercise: Exchange of Energy while Standing

Stand on both feet, with your weight distributed as evenly as possible. Let your attention go to your feet and look at them with your inward eye. Visualise your feet growing roots. See if you can see them with your inward eye. They reach down into the earth beneath you. Do they reach deep down, or not so deep?

However firmly your roots are planted, that is how you will stand, that is how you will be in life. Your very being will be coloured by these roots, and the way in which they connect with the earth which surrounds them.

It is the picture of your vitality, your consciousness, your attachment to matter and the state of your being. As a person grows 'below' so he develops 'above'.

The kind of roots a person has are an infallible guide to his whole state of development. It is not possible to deceive oneself here, because the nature of the roots cannot be influenced at will or by any kind of manipulation.

Any change in the roots towards strength, depth or better connection is possible only if one is stronger and deeper in one's own life and better connected to life itself.

The reverse is equally true. Any deterioration in the condition of the roots means a corresponding uprooting, preceded by a denial of life itself.

The roots are the indicator of the quality of life

The grounding process is an aid, a guide-line, a reliable mirror, by whose help the development of vitality, of life, is promoted, experienced and made possible.

This vitality is achieved only by someone who frees himself from all misleading images, from fantasy and thus from attachment to his own ego.

4.

The Body/Mind Connection of Man and his Feet

4. The body/mind Connection of Man and his Feet

Particular characteristics of a person's feet will give detailed information about his condition, both through the way they arise and the place where they occur. Also changes in these characteristics will indicate changes that are taking place in him.

The Tone of the Foot

The tone of the foot gives an insight into that person's inner vitality and vigour.

Hold the heel of someone's foot with your left hand and move the foot to and fro a few times, by means of the heel.

You will immediately get an impression of the inner tone of the foot and, through it, of the person as a whole.

If the movement is too loose, without inner vitality, you can assume from this that this person will similarly be lacking in vitality, in initiative of his own, in creative spontaneity and that he will be living without power and energy.

If the movement of the foot is difficult and jerky, or without an inner tone of its own, that person will be living as though he were cast in a mould. This indicates rigidity and self-

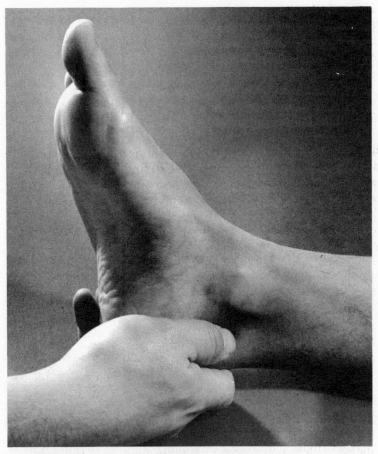

Photo A: Your right hand holding the heel of a foot.

constraint, a holding-on based on fear that he might lose control of his life and fall prey to outside influences. That is to say he has a low self-esteem. However, it is from this very need to control and restrain himself that these conflicts in his life and in the world around him arise, the very things he tries to avoid by his control.

If the movement of the foot has no definite tone, but it appears spongy and indistinct. This can also apply to the person as a whole, when the person's life will be joyless and indifferent.

The Musculature of the Foot

The musculature of the foot is closely connected with its tone. For example, it would be impossible to find a foot with loose tone and rigid musculature, because the distribution and flow of energy are reflected in the condition of the muscles.

You can find out the condition of the muscles of the foot by touching them and pressing gently. You will soon be able to feel which parts of the muscles in the foot are under low or high tension. Many muscles feel too narrow, others as though they had been blown up.

The condition of the muscles of the foot reflects the basic psychosomatic condition of the part of the person which is represented there (see diagram p. 23).

The Tendons

The foot is richly provided with tendons, which are the principle mechanical 'levers' of movement. They are the connecting links between the muscles and the bony structure. Their condition gives clues to the health of the power connections in the body. The achilles tendon and the flexor hallucis longus are particularly important in this respect.

The Flexor Hallucis Longus

The flexor hallucis longus is the tendon in the foot which connects the heel and the big toe. In a healthy foot it is responsible for the curve of the foot and thus for healthy contact between the earth and the heel, the ball of the foot and the toes.

On the physical level this tendon reflects the connection between head and pelvis, and on a level of 'higher' energy the condition of the psyche and its attachment to the earth.

Certain points along this tendon may sometimes by painful, indicating a disturbance in the relationship of head, pelvis and earthing.

The Achilles Tendon

It is primarily the achilles tendon which gives the foot its mobility and usefulness. It connects the calf muscles to the heel. It both represents attachment to the earth and reflects the connection of man with the outside world. A healthy achilles tendon indicates a person standing on his own two feet and at peace within himself, who no longer has any fear and is at rest in his centre, his pelvis.

Horny Skin

Horny or hardened skin arises when the whole foot, or certain parts of it, are under stress. The foot forms more hard-wearing skin, to protect it from rough ground. Horny skin which forms naturally extends over the whole sole of the foot. In spite of its hardness it should be flexible, and not thick enough to be a hindrance when walking or standing. Horny skin forms naturally today only among primitive peoples.

Horny skin which is unnaturally hard is caused by energy blocks and is found mostly on the heel, the ball of the foot and at the side of the big toe. Horny skin on the heel indicates a lack of connection between earth and man, while horny skin on the big toe indicates a disparity between man and his psyche. Horny skin signals an inward avoidance of true responsibility and authority in life.

Such horny skin usually indicates that insufficient attention is being paid to some particular aspect of life, or that it is even being neglected altogether.

Corns

Corns are caused by patches of hard skin which become packed to a dense point at their centre. Normally speaking, they are caused by pressure of footwear.

Corns are found mainly on the big toe and on the third and fourth toes. From the point of view of psychic energy, they often arise as a result of avoiding certain conflicts in ones's life. The corn is like a protective shield formed against the outside pressure.

The formation of a corn takes place from the outside inwards and can grow right to the bone, where it will cause intense pain.

If the conflict which caused the corn is not cleared up, the protective nature of the corn allows it to penetrate more and more deeply; and the pain which this causes is a constant reminder of the necessity to resolve the conflict.

This is the manner in which deep-seated mental conflicts are brought to the person's attention, in spite of his trying to avoid them.

Usually corns are mistakenly thought to grow inwards from the surface of the skin.

Lumps of Thickened Skin

Lumps of thickened skin, which look like little skin-mounds are found mostly on the arch of the foot and in the centre of the foot, in the zone of earth and life. They are emotional knots, containing pent-up emotions. These lumps of thickened skin are usually dark (reddish) in colour.

If they are resolved, the person involved will become emotionally richer.

Sweaty Feet

Chronic sweaty feet indicate an equally chronic psychic or physical overloading. The cause of this can be psychic or physical poisoning. The body tries to rid itself of the poison by continually secreting sweat.

Sweaty feet may also indicate continual emotional overloading, which is not allowed to come into the open, and does not show outwardly, and whose basic cause is never questioned, whether on account of its 'embarrassing' nature or through fear of the resulting consequences.

On the other hand, secretions of sweat lasting only a short time are healthy processes for cleansing energy.

Peeling Skin

Peeling skin is a sign of the shedding of an 'old skin', an old psychosomatic structure.

If the skin peels at a certain point, then a 'skin' is shed in that part of the person which is represented by this zone. The skin peeling over the whole foot shows the removal of a comprehensive structure in the truest sense of the word.

The old skin has become too tight for the growing individual so he sheds it.

No matter how or where this peeling takes place, it is an outward sign of progress in the direction of unity of body and mind in that person.

Discolouration of the Skin

Brownish Skin

Brownish discoloured skin is the sign of a deep-seated block caused by a lack of energy. The part of the body corresponding to the area of discolouration on the foot will be like a foreign organism, significant only in its function, lacking connection with the body as a whole.

This type of discolouration is usually found in the region of the achilles tendon, the arch of the foot and the big toe.

Milk-white Skin

Milk white skin in the foot region indicates unrealised aspects. It is quite common to find feet which are milk white all over. They give the impression of being life-less, inanimate. A person with such a foot does not live his own life; he feels himself being manipulated by external circumstances.

Blueish Skin

Blueish skin points to an unacknowledged, suppressed potential for aggression. However, since the rage lies only slightly below the surface, it can easily break out as the result of some trivial provocation.

Reddish Skin
It is important to distinguish between this and pink skin, which indicates a relatively good circulation.

The Temperature of the Foot

Cold Toes
Most people have cold toes which means that they are separated from the rest of the body.

Cold toes point to poor integration of the head/mind in the functioning of the body as a whole. The result of this is likely to be an either/or situation — living with the disturbing warmth of the emotions or the (usually more familiar) coolness of the head.

Chronic Cold Feet
A permanently cold foot is the sign of a super-cool life style. It is as though thought, action and emotion had been 'put on ice'.

Warm Feet of even Temperature
Warm feet of even temperature indicate health and harmony. Their owner stands with both feet on the ground; he is at peace with himself and goes on his way accepting and loving life.

Overheated feet
Overheated feet indicate overcharged, blocked emotions. This person is full of emotions he is unable to express in his life or release by means of an exchange of energy with the earth.

Depression of a Bone in the Metatarsus

The depression of a bone in the metatarsus shows that it has been inwardly strained by excess physical or emotional pressure. Usually the person's breathing will also be affected by this inner tension. He will find it difficult, an effort of will, to breathe deeply.

Exostosis

Exostosis is a superfluous growth, which indicates an inward desire to be more than one really is. It is caused by uncontrolled energy, which could be used positively to achieve greater stability.

Hammer Toes

Hammer toes are the expression of a cramped way of thinking, of a withdrawal from the outside world. The thoughts of a person with hammer toes are roundabout, complicated and involved. He likes to keep his thoughts to himself and also finds it difficult to make the contents of his thoughts and their results visible to others.

Broken Arches

Owing to this malformation of the foot, the flow of energy between foot and body may be poor or it may be lacking altogether. True earthing of energy is practically impossible.

A person with a broken arch is cut off by this break in his foot from his true way of life and its contents, or he has very little contact with them.

To put it another way: there exists a gap between the image he forms of himself and his true being, which can only be bridged with great difficulty by forming and developing a way of life in accordance with his true being.

Although, subjectively, he may get on well enough and feel all right, yet his fallen arches, which say 'no' to his true way of life and his own being, will bring him to latent discontent and uncertainty and to resulting unrest.

Fallen Arches

With fallen arches, the arches along the feet have fallen in. In the case of this abnormality of the feet, there will be a lack of positive charge from the shoulders to the pelvis, which becomes noticeable through lack of tone. Such people appear boring and feel bored.

Flat Feet

Flat feet may be caused by broken, fallen or spreading arches. In the case of spreading arches, the arches across the feet have fallen in.

With flat feet, there is a predominant need (in both the physical and the metaphorical sense) to be close to the 'dark hiding-place' of Mother Earth. Such a person does not go on his own path through life but wishes to 'go back'. He looks for symbiosis with his mother, and would like to return to the protection of her womb.

He feels inwardly heavily burdened. This inner heaviness often corresponds to his physical weight.

Since symbiosis between mother and child cannot be achieved and the man is both inwardly and outwardly heavy, he is unable to express himself in accordance with his needs.

The basic feeling is one of senselessness and hopelessness,

resulting in a hopelessly disordered life being created.

I have treated separately these indications of the body/ mind condition which are expressed in the feet so that I could describe them in detail.

However, any abnormality of the feet taken by itself does not tell you anything essential about the conditon of the person as a whole.

It is only when all the 'strengths' and 'weaknesses' of the feet are taken together and in conjunction with one another that a fundamental and comprehensive picture of the physical-mental blocks is obtained.

5.

A Structural Programme of Polarity Massage for the Feet

5. A structural Programme of Polarity Massage

This structural programme of polarity massage is arranged in such a way that all parts of a person are reached, harmonised, cleared of blocks and activated. With this end in view, a progressive sequence of hand contacts has been drawn up.

In the first phase, the foot is relaxed and prepared for the energies in the second phase.

In the second, the constructive energies are strengthened and the static energy which is blocked in the feet, and therefore, in the person as a whole, is made to flow again.

In the third and last phase, impulse is given throughout the massage to greater consciousness and more vitality and stability.

The whole massage programme and the individual contacts have been chosen in such a way that anyone wanting to work with polarity can easily carry them out. No special training is necessary.

It is, however, emphasised that the sequence of contacts and massages should be followed exactly, in order that:

physical and mental relaxation can be achieved

physical and mental blocks can be removed

the person being massaged can become more conscious and more awake

the person being massaged can be better able to feel his feet and the ground under his feet

the person being massaged can with each massage come a little closer to himself.

Finally after each massage, the person being massaged can arrive at greater vitality, greater harmony, grace and consciousness.

The massage session as a whole and the way the individual movements are carried out in it will vary from case to case, since each individual brings with him a different distribution of energy and his *own special* energy blocks.

The massage should, if possible, take place in a quiet room. Neither of the massage partners should have eaten too much or be hungry. Clothing should, as at all times, be made of natural materials, since these allow a better flow of energy.

Neither you, nor the person being massaged, should allow yourselves any expectation or preconceived idea about the massage but should simply let it work through the life energy.

The interval between individual massages should not be less than a week in order that the bodily energy may adapt itself to these penetrating massages. After at least five massages, the intervals may be shortened.

Before beginning massage, you should study the following chapter several times. Whilst doing so, it is helpful to visualise the various contacts and holds. This preliminary exercise will give you more assurance when you come to massaging your partner.

While you are doing the first few massages you might find it helpful to keep the book open so that you can check the exact contacts and their results. After a few massages performed in this way, you will be able to use the programme of polarity massage from memory.

Photo 1: Posture

At the beginning of the massage, focus on your partner's feet. Hold this attention without expecting anything in advance, but be aware.

You should retain this unjudgmental state of inner awareness throughout the massage. Your touch will set the energy flowing, the impulse which will have a natural tendency to balance itself. Vital energy obeys its own laws, which will be completely appropriate to the circumstances at every moment.

The First Phase
of the Programme

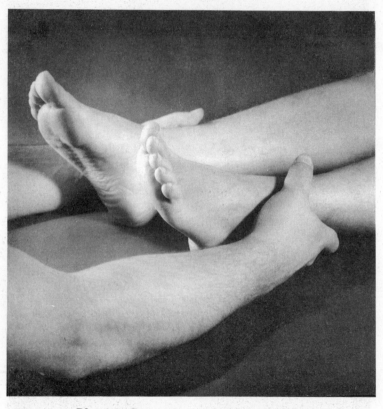

Photo 2: Grasp the feet behind the heels

Grasp the feet behind the heels and gently but firmly pull your partner towards you.

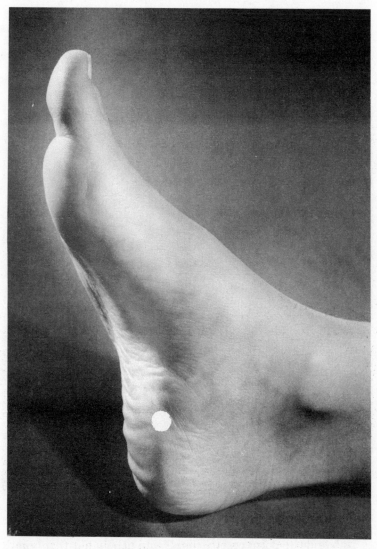

Photo 3: Pressure point

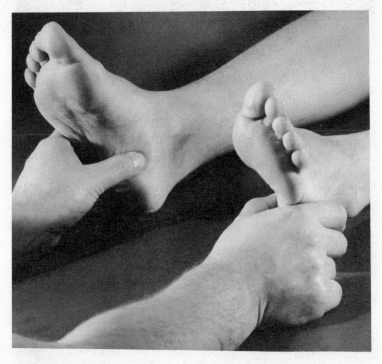

Photo 4: Pressing the points

Alternatively press the point on the left foot with your right thumb and the point on the right foot with your left thumb - five times each side, applying medium pressure.

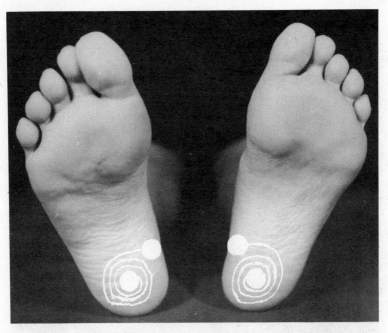

Photo 5: Direction of movement in heel massage

With strong pressure massage the ball of the heel on the left foot in a clockwise direction and the ball of the heel on the right foot in an anticlockwise direction in a spiral from the heel point you pressed on the page before to the centre of the heel. Finish off this massage with firm pressure on the centre of the ball of each heel.

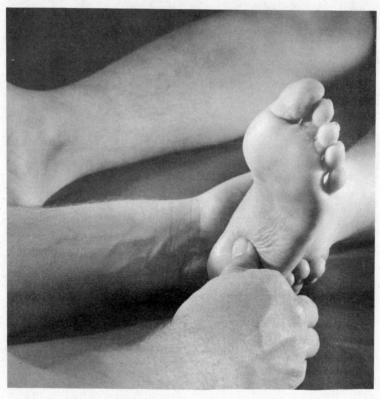

Photo 6: Heel massage

Carrying out the massage shown on photo 5.

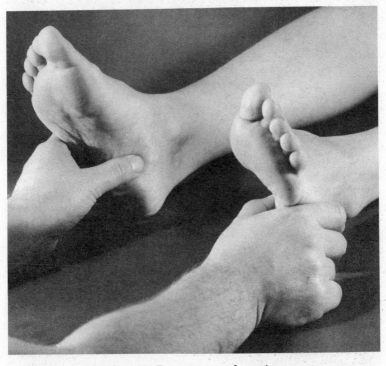

Photo 7: Pressure on the points

With your right thumb press the joint on the left foot, and with your left thumb the point on the right foot, three times each side alternately, using medium pressure.

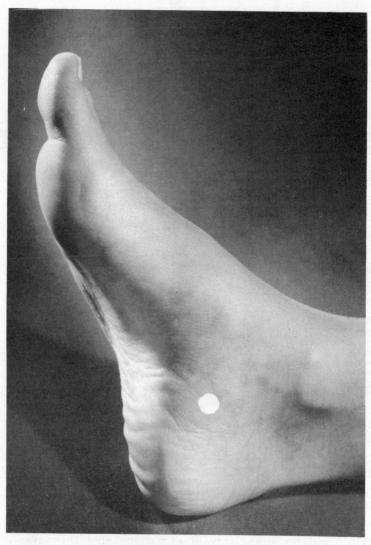

Photo 8: Pressure point on the inside of the heel

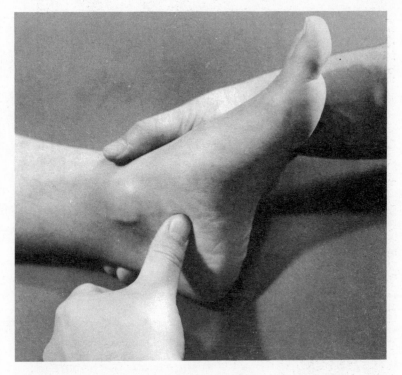

Photo 9: Pressing the point on the inside of the heel

Press these points on the inner sides of the heels just sufficiently strongly for the person being massaged not to feel an urge to pull his foot away if he feels any pain there.

Press the left foot with your thumb for 4 or 5 seconds and then the point on the right foot for 4 or 5 seconds.

While you are doing this, your partner should breathe deeply and freely, but without effort.

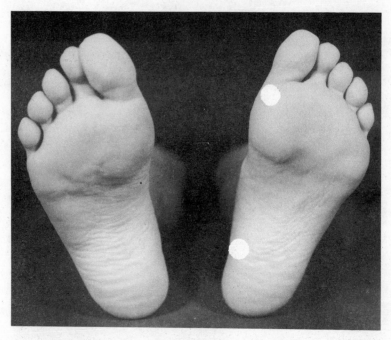

Photo 10: Left foot with pressure points 1 (top) and 2

Lay the forefinger of your right hand on point 1 and the forefinger of your left hand on point 2 of the left foot. In doing so, you should just touch the skin of the foot without applying any pressure.

While you are doing this, you should remain completely alert. Let the energies flow.

Listen for an inner prompting for when to remove your finger. The foot will actually tell you!

at all. If the place is too soft, without definite structure, you can assume that this person is cut off from the primordial source of matter. If the place is over-tense, as firm as steel, without any possibility of movement, then that person will be imprisoned in matter. He will no longer have any possibility of movement of his own accord. Any movement which does take place, how it resolves and its goal, will be dictated by force of circumstance.

If the point is over-soft it is, figuratively speaking, as if the person cannot reach sufficient formative material because he is too far away from matter. If it is overtense, the energy condition of this point does not allow for any new and original creation, but only for the old, rigid, uncreative models to be repeated again and again.

A healthy point of material energy gives a person unlimited possibilities of form, unshakeable confidence and perseverence and the possibility of expressing himself in and through matter by means of comprehensive and inexhaustable creativity.

Being (air)

The energy point of being lies in front of the foot, about two centimetres in front of the middle toes and has a diameter of about two and a half centimetres (diagram opposite). This point, too, is neither yin nor yang. It is as complete in itself as are the other three kinds of pure energy.

If the energy of this point remains in its indefinable, original state, that person has arrived safely at his life's goal. In that case he, too, can no longer be defined, he is all and nothing, unlimited and now.

Imbalances in and around this point indicate imbalances in the a person's state of being, his basic questioning about life. They are the essential questions which this man asks of humanity on life's path into the present.

The Point of Matter (earth)

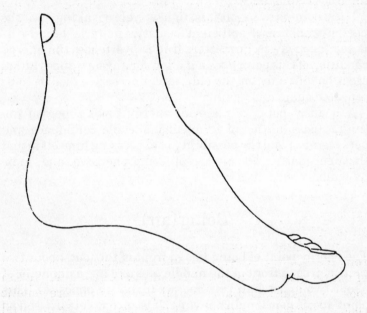

Matter (earth)

The point of material energy lies above the ankle, at the place where the achilles tendon and the calf muscle meet.

Pure matter is independent of our life, but it is essential that it should exist, before human life can receive a body. Pure matter is composed of atoms and molecules which vibrate at a certain frequency at balance within itself; it has no life yet is not without energy, has no consciousness, yet is with its own spirit.

Each manifestation of matter we know in daily life has its own vibrating frequency. Each object is a part and an expression of this primordial material. A flower has a different frequency from a stone, man has a different frequency from an animal.

One frequency is faster, another is slower: one is finer, another is coarser. They differ in the distance apart of their atomic particles and in the speed with which they reduce this distance.

This picture describes material power, which has already taken shape. It has been formed in accordance with the psycho-genetic code.

If all spaces, all distances disappear, then that which remains is pure matter. In a counter-movement, this density of matter gives rise to the whole multiplicity of life. We can look on this primordial material power as the pre-genetic code, as the potential of all that is formed. It is the material zero point containing all the possibilities of form, limitless, without information about the future or the past.

If this point at the end of the achilles tendon and the beginning of the calf muscle is pressed, almost everyone will have some sort of reaction.

Pressure on this point usually produces pain or the consciousness of being devoid of feeling. You often feel too much tension on the surface of the body or else scarcely any tension

The Point of
Consciousness (water)

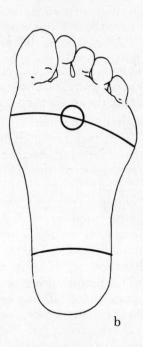

b

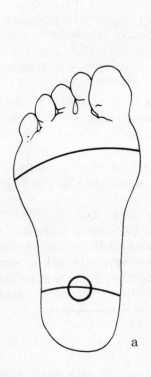

a

The Life Energy
Point (fire)

Energy Points (Elements)

The Life Energy (fire)

The region indicated on the diagram "a" opposite is neither yin nor yang. It is the region of concentrated life energy. It is neutral, neither positively nor negatively charged. The primordial substance of all life lies hidden in this point.

This point represents life, vitality in material things and in the human being. It lies significantly on the line which divides and at the same time unites the earthly region and the region of the life of man. It touches equally the yin and yang halves of the foot.

Consciousness (water)

Another region of the foot which shows neither a yin nor a yang charge is the pont of consciousness/clarity (diagram "b" opposite). It lies on the vertical line which touches and divides the regions of psyche and of life.

Many people have thick, horny skin in this region. This may be taken as a sign of consciousness not fully developed, as a refusal to extend consciousness to earthly, everyday things. Tension in this region is a sign of a lack of consciousness or of a 'conscious' desire of the mind to keep aloof, a rigid retreat from worldly things.

it and the earth, a distancing from worldly events.

The outside edge of the foot is quite different. In a healthy foot there is complete contact with the earth and with reality. This part is harder than the inside of the foot. Here are found points reflecting the external organs.

It will bring about a physical change corresponding to an area of weakness in the body.

Thought, feeling and action are forced into a rigid pattern.

As a result of what has happened, consciousness will be reduced for as long as the effect lasts.

The free flow of energy is stopped.

Change in physical form, mental rigidity and dullness are all the result of structures which leave their mark on the level of physical energy. Almost everyone will take these structures to be his own ego-identity, his own way of living, his strengths and weaknesses.

However, these structures contribute nothing to that person and are even a hindrance to him. They form his identity, the mask or persona, from behind which he only seldom peeps out. The very word 'identity' implies the identification with a mask. People will then say things like: "I am a social worker, I am this and that ..., I am restless/calm, I am kind, good/bad," etc. Attitudes which arise as a result of mechanical structures are: "I must ... I can't ... I wouldn't do such a thing ..." and these lead to corresponding action signals.

The human being is made free by being liberated from his blocks.

One view is that these blocks are present in principle throughout the whole body. Another view is that each block has 'its' definite place in 'its' corresponding organ of the body.

Both views are justified. A block, no matter where it is situated, can colour and direct a person's whole body and his entire life. A block can dictate the how, why and wherefore and the very goal of existence.

Polarity and Life Energy

Stagnant energy, which blocks the life energy, was itself formerly free-flowing vital energy. Its flow was impaired by some experience of individual stress or trauma which reduced consciousness. The stressfulness of the block depends both on the intensity of the experience and on the degree of consciousness or its absence.

If it were possible to have full consciousness, then a particularly stressful experience may have very little influence on the flow of vital energy. However, if the person is at a low level of awareness, an insignificant event, which another person would hardly notice, may arrest the flow of vital energy altogether.

Consciousness and the life energy serve one another. The level of consciousness influences the quality and amount of the life energy.

The life energy is an ever-flowing fountain of youth, which is never exhausted. It is nothing less than boundlessness and vitality. Life energy, unaccompanied by conscious awareness, is like a multi-coloured world of the emotions, like a firework continually sparkling in the most beautiful colours. If it flows along without consciousness, it is just formless and chaotic creativity, without sense or purpose.

Consciousness without vitality is like a functional house, designed and built according to purely objective criteria. It is entirely practical, but it lacks the colour and variety which people would call beautiful, vital and wonderful. This life energy promotes consciousness and enlivens it with its endless variety.

Any situation where a reduction in consciousness coincides with some stressful experience will leave its mark on the life energy, which may even become blocked. This is seen in four ways:

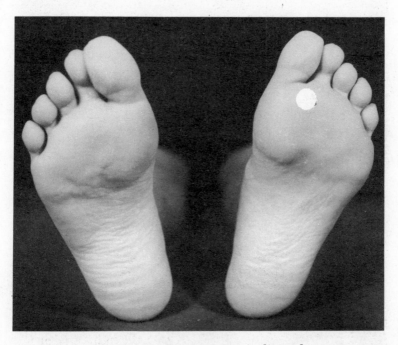

Photo 13: Pressure point indicated

With your right thumb press hard on the middle of the inner edge of the heel, and at the same time with your left thumb, press hard on the central point between the ball of the foot and the toes, and between the big toe and the second toe. Begin with the left foot and press *once only*.

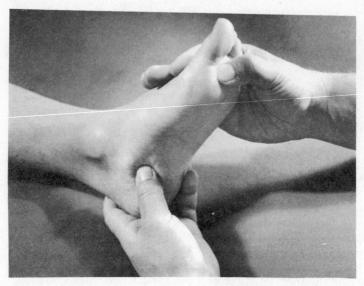

Photo 14: The contact with the left foot

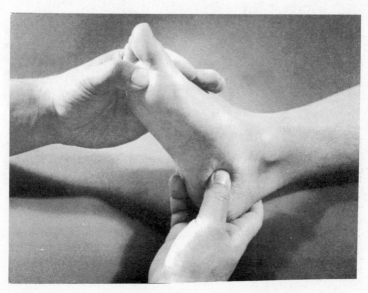

Photo 15: The contact with the right foot

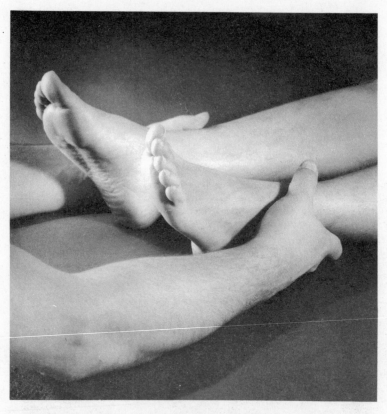

Photo 16: Grasp the feet behind the heels

Grasp the feet behind the heels and pull the legs gently but firmly towards you.

If you feel any resistance, accept this, and do not pull any more.

Put the feet down again gently.

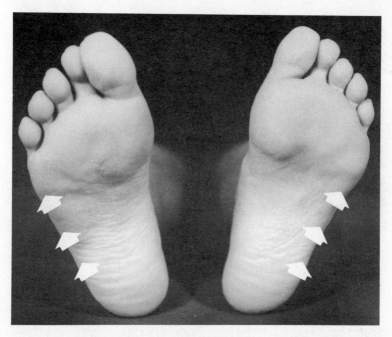

Photo 17: Direction of movement for massaging

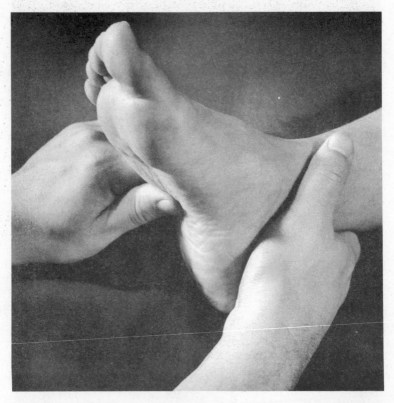

Photo 18: Your thumb massages the outside edge of the foot

Hold the foot with your right hand. Pressing firmly, move your left thumb along the outside edge of the left foot, beginning above the heel, up to the ball of the foot.

Carry out this movement three times in succession on each foot, beginning with the left. Take care that your thumb does not go up to the toes.

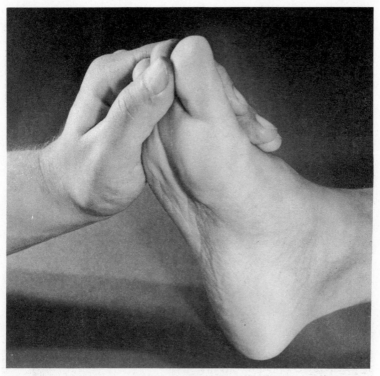

Photo 19: Pulling the smaller toes

Pull toes 2 to 5 together upwards, first on the *right* foot and then on the left. Pull them upwards until the heel is still just in contact with the ground, not so that you click the joint.

After these massage contacts, you should pause for at least five minutes, in order to give your partner the opportunity of sensing his feet and listening more deeply within himself. During this break, the person who is being massaged should remain lying down.

The Second Phase
of the Programme

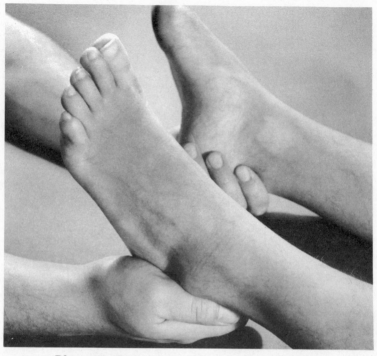

Photo 20: Carrying out the contact on both feet

After the break begin again with the following contact:

With your thumb and forefinger, hold the foot in the centre of the triangle formed by the achilles tendon, the heel and the ankle bone.

In this contact, it is important that your hands should not apply pressure, since energy here flows better without pressure.

Don't try to imagine what is happening. Inwardly adopt the attitude that you will allow whatever wants to happen.

No effort of will, or any other kind of effort, is necessary. Here, again, watch carefully for the moment when you should quietly remove your hands.

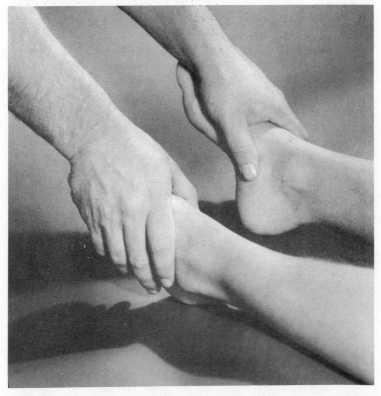

Photo 21: Hands on the insteps

Place your right hand on the bottom part of your partner's left instep and your right hand on the instep of his right foot. Let the energy flow.

Watch for the moment when you should release your hands.

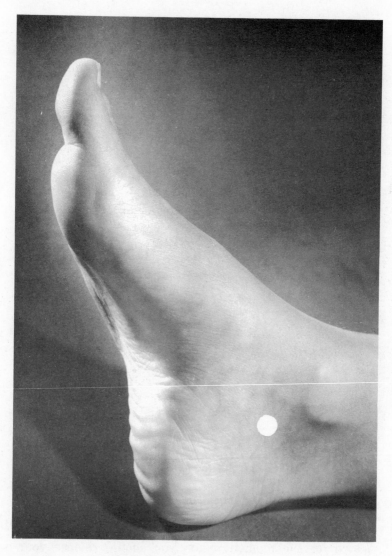

Photo 22: Pressure point

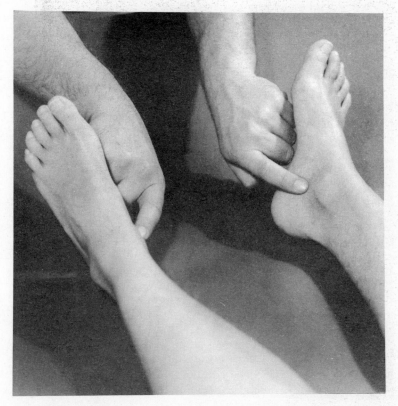

Photo 23: Polarisation of the points

Place your right forefinger lightly about half an inch below the ankle of the left foot in the direction of the sole. Your left forefinger should be placed on the corresponding spot on the right foot.

Let the energy flow.

Watch for the exact moment when you should release your fingers.

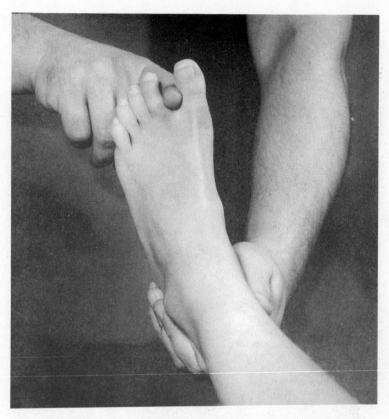

*Photo 24: Your right forefinger between the big toe
and the second toe*

Place the first joint of your right forefinger between the big
toe and the second toe of your partner's left foot.

Leave it in that position for about a minute and a half. Do
not exert any pressure, simply wait to see what happens.

Then place the first joint of the same *right* finger between
the big toe and the second toe of your partner's right foot.

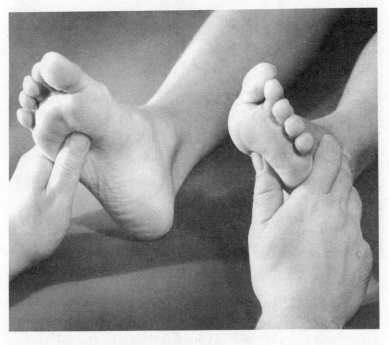

Photo 25: Your thumbs under the balls of the feet

Press gently on each foot alternately ten to fifteen times, exactly in the centre of the ball of the foot.

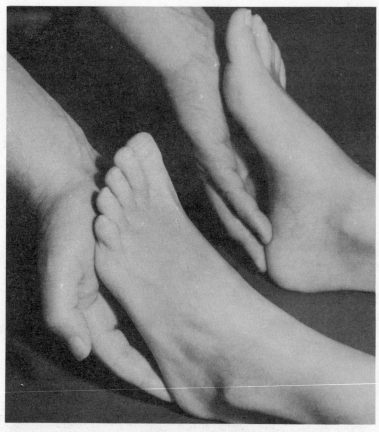

Photo 26: Your hands lie on the soles of the feet

Place the ball of the thumb of your right hand on the ball of the left foot. Let your fingers rest on the heel.

Similarly place the ball of your left thumb on the ball of the right foot and your fingers on the heel.

Let the energy flow.

Watch for the moment when it seems right to take your hands away.

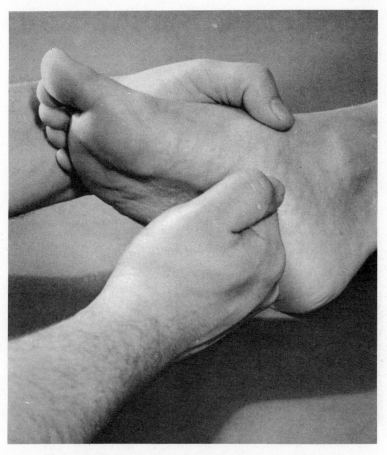

Plate 27: Pulling above the sole of the foot with your knuckles

Make your hand into a fist, and with the pressure of your knuckles stroke over the sole of the foot from the centre of the heel to the centre of the ball of the foot. Repeat this movement two or three times on each foot.

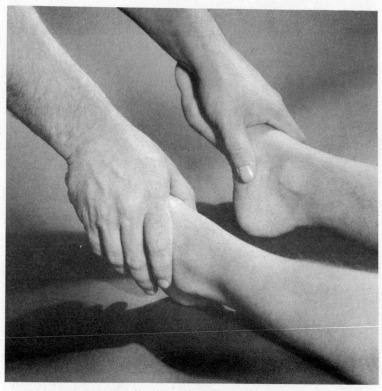

Photo 28: Your hands lie on the lower part of the instep

Place your right hand on the lower part of your partner's left instep and your left hand on the lower part of his right instep.

Let the energy flow.

Watch for the moment when it seems right to take your hands away.

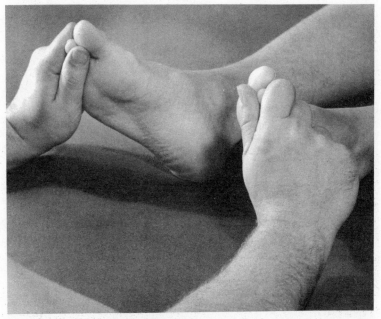

Photo 29: Your hands clasp the toes

Place your right hand round all the toes of the left foot, except the big toe, and your left hand round all the toes of the right foot, except the big toe.

Let the energy flow until the moment comes when you should take your hands away. After this contact, take a break of at least ten minutes. If you have become tense during this massage, you can use this time to relax and feel whole again.

The Third Phase
of the Programme

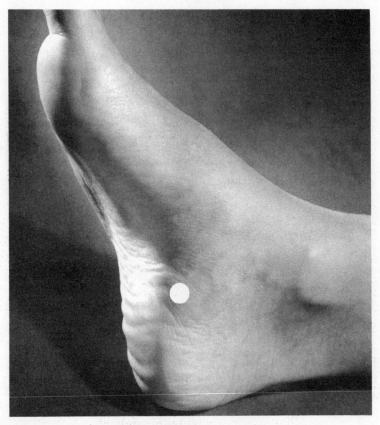

Photo 30: Pressure point

Hold your right forefinger about an inch above the energy point on the left foot, just high enough to be in contact with the energy.

Feel for the energy flow.

Here again, watch for the moment when it seems right to take your finger away.

Then hold your *right* finger again above the point on the right foot.

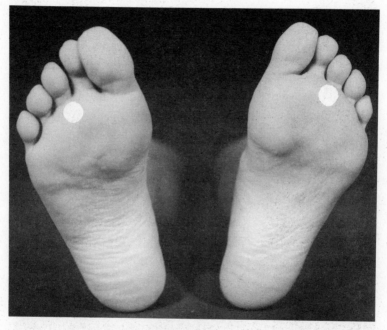

Photo 31: Pressure points indicated

Hold the forefinger of your right hand about an inch above the centre of the left foot, between the ball of the foot and the toes, at a height where you are just in contact with the energy.

Hold the left index finger above the same spot on the right foot, again just high enough to be in contact with the energy.

Allow the energy to flow through both fingers.

Take your fingers away at the right moment.

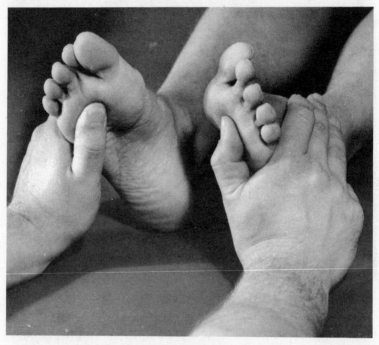

Photo 32: Pulling your thumbs over the centre of the ball of the foot

As soon as you have taken your fingers away, pull your thumbs with fairly strong pressure over the centre of the ball of the foot, from the tip of the toes to the beginning of the metatarsus.

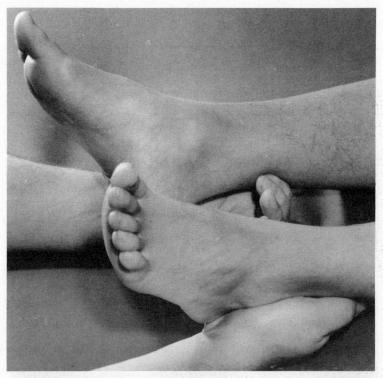

Photo 33: Massage of the point of matter on both feet

Massage the point of matter between the achilles tendon and the beginning of the calf muscles for half a minute to a minute. You will know inwardly whether you should massage this point firmly, lightly or with alternating, but always rhythmic, pressure.

You will find this out if you open yourself inwardly to these possibilities and let the movements of your hands be guided by their own intelligence and not by the head.

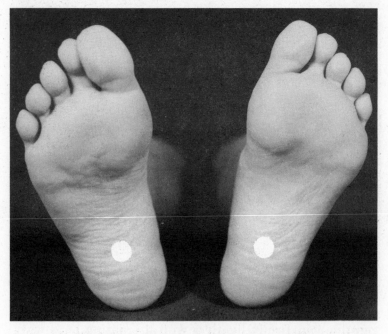

Photo 34: The energy points indicated

Press the two life energy points really hard for a few seconds with your two thumbs.

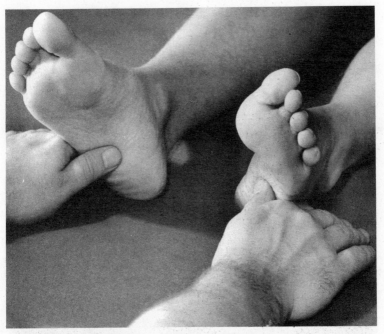

Photo 35: Pressing the energy points

The positon of your hands is shown here. If you do a graduated polarity foot massage programme with children and adolescents, the matter point at the end of the achilles tendon and the beginning of the calf muscles should *not* be massaged.

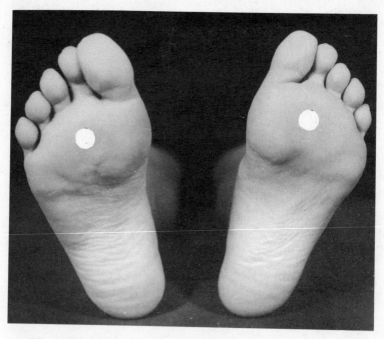

Photo 36: The 'consciousness' pressure points indicated

In the case of children and adolescents, end with light pressure with both forefingers simultaneously on the 'consciousness' points.

6.

Open
Polarity Massage

6. Open Polarity Massage

The basic attitude you should adopt during massage is *Awareness*. At the same time, *you should let the energy flow*.

When you massage the feet by the polarity method, be constantly alert and inwardly conscious. Your attention should be directed both towards yourself *and* towards your partners feet.

Thoughts and distractions disturb your consciousness and the flow of vital energy.

During the massage, don't think about the why and the wherefore of what you are doing.

Be alert and let your movements flow with and through the life energy.

If you take these basic principles to heart, every massage session will be simple for you and harmonising for your massage partner. In this way, you will be able to give your partner the best possible treatment in your power at that moment.

The more alert and open you are, the clearer and more definite your movements will be and the more penetrating the harmonising changes in the person being massaged.

This means that the quality of the massage depends on your consciousness and on your openness to the life energy.

It is advisable for you to be positioned comfortably on the ground (see Exchange of Energy while Standing: p) and to recollect yourself. This promotes inner alertness and sureness.

During massage, it is helpful to pay attention to your physical posture (release your tensions!) and, if possible, consciously to breathe deeply and regularly, but without any strain, during the whole massage.

Next, some exercises and techniques by means of which greater alertness and openness may be achieved.

Have a polarity foot masssage done to yourself frequently.

Repeat the positioning exercise frequently.

The more grounded you are, the easier it will be for you to be alert and open. The exercise 'walking in harmony' is particularly good for raising the level of energy.

Here is an exercise which promotes inner calm and attentiveness, while at the same time increasing sensitivity towards physical energy:

Exercise: Becoming more Realistic

Stand, preferably barefoot, and look into yourself.

Observe how your energy is distributed. Begin with your head, then your shoulders, your arms, your chest, etc. Take stock for a moment. Observe, but do not judge.

After looking at the way energy is distributed through all the parts of your body, let your roots grow down from your feet and let an exchange of energy take place with the earth.

While walking and sitting, concentrate on your feet.

This exercise will, in the long run, make you more realistic and more positive.

Go barefoot as often as possible.

Continually remember yourself; call to mind the fact that you are alive and vital. This will make you conscious of yourself.

During massage, feelings of insecurity, discontent and inadequacy will keep recurring. You may, perhaps, also have thoughts such as these: "I should use this or that contact now . . . surely this or that should happen now . . . this contact or this touch seems to me more significant than the one I can see with my inner eye, (etc) . . ."

In such situations, take care not to be caught up in an inner dialogue which will certainly be fruitless, will rob you of your energy, will in a sense let you fall inwardly asleep and will render you relatively incapable of action.

Such thoughts and feelings arise to some extent because, through heightened awareness and through surrendering oneself to the guidance of the life energy, the corresponding doubts are inevitably activated.

If this happens, there are various things which can be done: to my mind, the best thing is not to allow yourself to be led astray by any thoughts or feelings, but to become inwardly calm and quiet, to increase your alertness and to entrust yourself confidently to the direction and guidance of the life energy.

It will then be just as if the effects of the blocks were to disappear.

Another possibility is to break off the massage for a short time, to ground yourself, release the surplus (static) energy and to let an exchange of energy with the earth really take effect.

If you allow the polarity of earth and man to become fully effective, this can also lead to the resolution of confused thoughts and feelings, or it can at least calm them for the moment. These thoughts and feelings, the inner dialogue, can sometimes become so strong that it is advisable to take a longer break in the massage or to end that particular session altogether.

In the meantime, you can then get to work on the blocks which are hindering you, and either get rid of them, or at least render them harmless. Keep reminding yourself during the massage to breathe deeply and calmly, without effort.

Life energy communicates itself in various ways. It appears

to be connected with your astrological makeup tells you nothing about the quality of its guidance or the quality of the massage.

It may be that you will know the right contacts or positions to use without seeing or finding a rational explanation for them.

Sometimes a particular contact or a particular way of placing your fingers and your hands may appear before you in a mental image. At other times you may feel that a particular contact, a particular way of touching, is appropriate.

It does not matter how it is communicated to you, the important thing is that you should act exactly in accordance with what you receive.

Be careful to put your finger or your hand in the exact place you see with your inner eye, where it feels right, or where you know it should be.

It is only then that the helpful impulse, which is available to your massage partner to release his blocked energy and to strengthen his consciousness and his vital energy, can take effect at the right moment.

It is, therefore, essential that the contacts and movements should be carried out exactly, if the work is to be effective. The required precision sought after is that of conscious work, which gives you, as masseur, the best possible means of distancing yourself from your own mechanisms and gives the person being massaged the impulse towards development which is right and appropriate for that moment.

Inwardly you will feel the difference between this and incorrect execution of the contacts. This imprecision makes you feel discontented and also gives rise to the feeling that something is not quite right and could be done better.

Such a vague feeling is usually not the consequence of a block, but is rather the life energy calling on you to work more consciously and more precisely.

If you carry out the massage in accordance with the demands of the life energy, you will also be able to feel this. It will be communicated to you by a sense of contentment and by the certainty that you have done a really useful piece of work.

If, as masseur, you surrender yourself completely to the guidance of the life energy and perform the contacts and movements exactly, you will inwardly be calmer, more composed and more concentrated.

Part of your precision and reliability consists in knowing the right moment to take your hands away and the moment when the whole massage should stop.

Each person has a different time for reaching the limit, when his potential for change and develpment has become exhausted.

The wisdom of the life energy within us knows this measure. It enables everyone to make just the right amount of progress which is possible at that moment.

When you 'hear' the 'signal' to stop, given by the life energy, it means that the point has been reached beyond which this massage partner can no longer develop for the moment. To continue any longer would at best lead to no result at all and at worst would confuse the energies again and mean that this massage partner would be partially or completely overloaded.

In order to be able to carry out this open polarity massage of the feet with precision, it is important to have had plenty of practice working to a routine.

When practicing your massage, you can learn to become more aware. You can become more sensitive to the energies and learn to listen for the exact 'stop signal' from the life energy.

In order to allow the possibilities of development offered by this kind of foot massage to become more penetrating, the person being massaged should look within himself during the foot massage and should observe without judgement.

In this way he will make himself more sensitive to what is

happening within him, and he will become more conscious. He will be able to accept more readily the changes and development connected with them, and his greater alertness will enable him to develop further.

He should look at what is happening to him, as long as it does not take his breath away (literally and metaphorically) and should let it pass before his eyes like a movie. As soon as the person being massaged interferes with what is happening, or lets himself be influenced by it, he halts the liberating process and stops the healing power of the life energy.

The process of development is likewise interrupted if the person being massaged tries to understand the images, feelings, thoughts or physical reactions which arise by thinking about them analyticallly. If it occurs during the actual massage this desire to understand rationally should be seen as a blocking of energy.

Everyone can understand these inner reactions if he goes along with them, accepting them, and at the same time emphatically affirming this development.

After massage, it is not usually necessary to work through these inner experiences. It is unnecessary because during the massage a great deal will have resolved itself of its own accord and also because open polarity massage of the feet, as presented here, will have activated the powers of self-healing, which will continue even after the massage is over.

In foot massage carried out in accordance with the principles stated above, the life energy is active to just the extent required for development to take place.

Open polarity massage of the feet, carried out on the basis of inward alertness and guided by the life energy, gives the person being massaged an impulse towards development which is possible, perhaps even necessary, and is certainly exactly right for that particular moment.

What does Massage do?

Any kind of polarity massage of the feet will increase the sense of bodily harmony.

Hampering defence mechanisms on physical, psychic and spiritual levels are resolved and enjoyment of life, love of peace and a sympathetic approach to others are promoted.

How far anyone proceeds on this way to inner freedom, to harmony and to love may depend on external circumstances, on his limitations and his own efforts. Polarity massage of the feet offers this possibility.

Progress towards greater harmony is a process in tune with time. Many familiar and favoured ways of thought, actions, and emotions will be relinquished and will disappear.

This letting go may not always be easy. Every time one gives up something which has been held for a long time, this brings a little more life, more energy and vitality, more consciousness on the way to freedom, to inner peace, which is necessary before we can obtain the external freedom and peace for which we are striving.

7.

The Chakras
and the Feet

7. The Chakras and the Feet

The condition of the body chakras is also reflected in the feet.

The chakras may be seen as regulators of energy between the inside and the outside. They indicate and adjust the balance of inward and outward life, of vitality. If they are impaired in their capacity to fulfil these functions, we shall also find an impairment in the physical energy and the social life of the person concerned.

For example, if the heart chakra is in a state of imbalance, that person will apply himself only to the extent allowed by the amount that this chakra can function; and to the extent that one applies oneself and loves oneself, so one will also love (or not love) one's fellow humans.

As a variation of the old saying: 'As above, so below' one could say here: 'As within, so without'.

According to whether the inner condition is flowing or not flowing, so also the life, whose organisation can be seen on the outside and its quality will either be flowing or not flowing. The mediator between inside and outside is the chakra.

Seen as a whole, each person has only one chakra, his body. However, the body chakra is not the person himself, but is the regulator of energy, the mediator and the reflected image of inside and outside. We are, therefore, in our body/mind chakra and at the same time we are not in it.

The body will often be experienced as a boundary, since it is not open to what comes from outside. If it is thus experienced, then disturbances and blockages will be present.

The Chakras of the whole body (Yang) – Right Foot

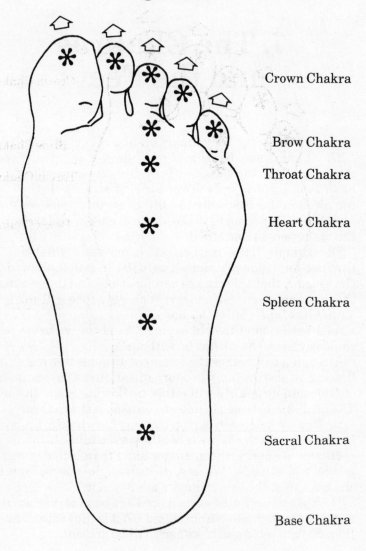

Crown Chakra

Brow Chakra

Throat Chakra

Heart Chakra

Spleen Chakra

Sacral Chakra

Base Chakra

The Chakras of the Whole Body (Yin) – Left Foot

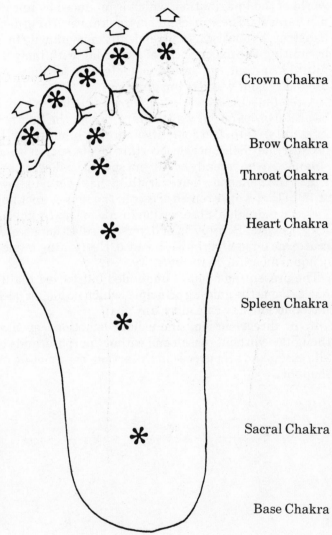

Crown Chakra

Brow Chakra

Throat Chakra

Heart Chakra

Spleen Chakra

Sacral Chakra

Base Chakra

There is no real outside or inside to a person. The idea of a sovereign and separate existence arises through the inner world of the imagination, which is produced by unconscious mechanisms. These mechanisms make everything dark, lead us astray, hypnotise us and render us momentarily incapable by uniting the experiences of yesterday with images of the future, so that we orient ourselves according to these products of our world of imagination.

Attending classes/workshops or reading books may indeed be useful props on our way to unity, but for the final step into humanity, into freedom, they are a hindrance. This is because they hold energy at certain levels, so that something stagnates which really could and should be flowing.

Just the moment when everything has begun to flow, all is still. In that way, even an arrest in the flow cannot happen.

Every individual observation inside me and outside me no longer exists. Perception of diversity, selection according to reason no longer has any relevance. Everything is one and is of equal meaning in its diversity.

The present moment of undivided but varied reality, has now become the guiding principle, which no longer needs any introduction, any causality, any goal.

It is direct action, immediate emotion, spontaneous thought – without reason and without purpose, and yet with all reason and all purpose in the action, the emotion and the thought.

Appendix: Care of the Feet

There is a simple and usually very pleasant way of caring for the feet: simply to go barefoot (but being careful not to injure them).

Blocked energies in the feet are affected by the greater possibility of movement in the feet and are eventually made to flow. Further, through the greater attention paid to the feet when going barefoot, the energies blocked in the upper parts of the body – the chest, shoulders, nape of the neck and head – are drawn downwards – to the belly, the diaphragm, the legs and the feet. The result is a harmonious distribution of energy throughout the whole body.

In the climate and environment in which we live, going barefoot is often inappropriate. We therefore need well-fitting footwear. Cheap shoes often cost the wearer dearly. High heels lead in the long run to faulty posture in the region of the diaphragm and the spine. If anyone wears plastic shoes (also shoes with plastic soles) the exchange of energy between the earth and that person cannot take place easily. This is comparable to synthetic clothing, which makes it difficult for the skin to breathe.

A good shoe should allow enough room for the toes and give good support to the heel. The shoe should adapt itself to the foot and be made in such a way that it takes on the shape of the foot.

In the case of many shoes, I have the feeling that it is the other way round: the foot has taken on the shape of the shoe.

Attention should also be paid to the socks. These should, if possible, be made of natural fibres which will allow the feet to breathe and perspire better.

Another possible way of caring for the feet is with foot baths. Many such baths can be bought ready made up at a pharmacy, but, with a little knowledge and a feeling for herbs, oils and tinctures and the effects they have on the organism, it is possible for anyone to concoct such a bath himself.

Herbal baths have the advantage that you can make them up individually, so that they balance and regulate the distribution of energy in the feet and in the individual as a whole.

Here is one mixture to try: A refreshing coltsfoot bath invigorates and strengthens the feet and stabilises the flow of vital energy:

1 handful dried coltsfoot leaves
1 handful of fresh green coltsfoot leaves

Boil down the dried coltsfoot leaves in 1 litre of water, fill up with warm water and bathe your feet liberally in it. Then place the green coltsfoot leaves on your feet and bind them on with a gauze bandage. This should stay on for one or two hours. This treatment is particularly good for feet which are swollen after standing for a long time.

The best care which anyone can give to his feet is to adopt a positive and affectionate attitude towards himself as a whole. This is an affirmation of his own way of life and of the possibilities of development which lie within him. This is made possible living with and in his feet, which are both stable and flexible at the same time.